Long Spurred
Columbine

The Treasury of
VICTORIAN
Flowers
The Daily Journal

Creative Publishing

*T*his Address Book contains text and Illustrations carefully researched from the Antiquarian Archive of Robert F. Hicks, the creator and publisher of this book. The texts and illustrations are among the very best of their day, taken from the golden period of illustration commencing around 1860, and hold a period charm and colour that can delight us afresh.

The texts themselves are extracts which contain a good deal of the then prevailing knowledge of the subject both general and scientific and they express many opinions in an entertaining and lively manner.

This Edition
© Creative Publishing
Old Orchard Street
Bath BA1 1JU
This Edition First Published 1997
All Rights Reserved
Illustrations and texts
© Creative Publishing

Design, Colour separations and Typesetting by Creative Publishing
ISBN 1-85081-021-4
Printed by Man Sang Envelope Manufacturing Co. Ltd. China

*C*ontributors to the Text and Illustrations:

The texts are a collection of writings by well known botanical authors, and by inspirational poets mainly of North America. The Illustrations are an impressive collection of works by L. Clarkson who portrayed the woods and plants of Maryland, H. G. Moon, a fine botanical artist as shown in many large Plates, and the versatile Maud Angell whose fine pencil and wash drawings are scattered throughout this book, along with some of her writings to students in magazine articles. Her Editor writes;

"To love the little things that God has made cannot fail to bring us a step nearer to the Creator. And Miss Angell's 'talks' help us to see these little things—the ground-ivy flower, the jasmine twig, the crimson on the back of the rose-leaf, the beauty of the dry dead stalks in the November hedgerow—just the commonplaces that we might so easily pass unnoticed, the commonplaces that become wonderments when we do notice them."

Design and concept by Creative Publishing, at their Bath studio in the U.K.

This Daily Journal Gift Book

Was Presented to ....

by ....

as a treasury for recording personal details of

relatives and friends who we

remember on many occasions, bearing in mind

our love for the natural world and the

family of Flowers, in all their many beautiful

forms and seasons.

This Journal enables you, with your diary dates to hand, to fill in and record important events on a weekly basis using the 52 available entry pages - these are not dated on the page which makes it possible to commence the Journal at any time, and indeed to continue to use it for recording purposes over several years while still enjoying the beauty of the presentation.

	Month	Dates	Week ....

Monday	*The Daily Journal*
Tuesday	*The Daily Journal*
Wednesday	*The Daily Journal*
Thursday	*The Daily Journal*
Friday	*The Daily Journal*
Saturday	*The Daily Journal*
Sunday	*The Daily Journal*

The Wild Rose

Shown opposite is the wild Dog-Rose found abundantly over Great Britain and Ireland. Apart from the Roses wild, there are at least fifty other species scattered all over the temperate and subtropical world. The wild species are not so common in America, and extend South as far as Mexico, Abyssinia, and the East Indian Peninsula. The Rose, has long been the acknowledged "Queen of Flowers," and it is also the floral emblem of England. Then, as a type of Beauty and Love, it was dedicated to Venus. Cupid is said to have given the Rose as a bribe to Harpocrates, the God of Silence, whence in part comes our modern expression "sub rosa," or "under the Rose." The cultivation and improvement of the Rose is an important industry in Europe and America to-day, as it has been in the East from time immemorial. In Arabia, in Persia, and in Cashmere, the Rose has long been valued not for its beauty alone, but also as the source of the precious Attar, or Otta of Roses, one of the oldest and most delicious of manufactured perfumes. We might easily fill an entire volume with the poetry of the Rose, since all the poets mention it when they mention flowers.

OCTOBER SNOW

*TO LONGFELLOW ON HIS
SEVENTIETH BIRTHDAY*

GEORGE P. LATHROP

CAME once a dim October night
So still the season's quiet flow
Seemed there to pause, as if it might
In ripples back to summer go.

The heavy dusk in dreams like flowers
Unfolded thoughts of endless ease:
Loss was no more; life's coming hours
Drove winter hence with melodies.

But keen-eyed Day through frostier air
Beheld a swift age overgrow
Those flower-like dreams—for everywhere
The night had whitened into snow !

Yet youthful still the trees arose;
And leaves consumed with autumn-fire
Blushed underneath the scattered snows
With colors of the Spring's desire.

And still with sweet defiance rang
A late-voiced songster's echoing note:
Time altered not the strain he sang,
Nor quenched the summer in his throat.

So in the days of youth you wrought
A spell with Voices of the Night,
And left our hearts with flower-dreams fraught,
And hush'd the seasons in their flight.

And if too soon the hoar frost throngs
Your air, O Poet of our prime,
It seeks in vain to chill your songs
Or blanch the beauty of your rhyme !

Monday

The Daily Journal

Tuesday

The Daily Journal

Wednesday

The Daily Journal

Thursday

The Daily Journal

Friday

The Daily Journal

Saturday

The Daily Journal

Sunday

The Daily Journal

Week ....

Month MAY   *Dates*

Trailing rose

Monday	*The Daily Journal*
Tuesday	*The Daily Journal*
Wednesday	*The Daily Journal*
Thursday	*The Daily Journal*
Friday	*The Daily Journal*
Saturday	*The Daily Journal*
Sunday	*The Daily Journal*

Month	Dates	Week ....

Monday

The Daily Journal

Tuesday

The Daily Journal

Wednesday

The Daily Journal

Thursday

The Daily Journal

Friday

The Daily Journal

Saturday

The Daily Journal

Sunday

The Daily Journal

Notes & Records

Daffodils

The Cowslip or Paigle

Besides adding much to the springtide beauty of our meadows and woods, the Cowslip and the common Primrose have also contributed not a little to our garden flora. Now, although it is quite possible to find Cowslips in woods and copses and under hedges, and Primroses here and there in the open meadows, yet, as a general rule, the reverse is more often true, and you find the Cowslips happiest and most abundant in sunny meadows, and Primroses more common in lightly shaded woods. This is a common trait amongst species of the same genus; they do not huddle together, but spreading afield, each takes up the habitat for which it is best fitted, and so is enabled to survive in the great struggle for food and space that is always going on in the world of flowers. No one appears to know the derivation of either Paigle or Cowslip, though Ben Jonson speaks of "Bright days-eyes, and the lips of Cowes," and suggests that we may rest contented that it is a child of the meadows, and that its balmy scent recalls the sweet breath of cows as they lie at rest in the sun after their dinner of tender herbage washed in dew. Shakespeare had observed the bees among the Cowslip flowers, and it is perhaps to them that we owe the numerous hybrids that have been produced

Monday

The Daily Journal

Tuesday

The Daily Journal

Wednesday

The Daily Journal

Thursday

The Daily Journal

Friday

The Daily Journal

Saturday

The Daily Journal

Sunday

The Daily Journal

Long Spurred
Columbine

Month	Dates	Week ....

Monday

The Daily Journal

Tuesday

The Daily Journal

Wednesday

The Daily Journal

Thursday

The Daily Journal

Friday

The Daily Journal

Saturday

The Daily Journal

Sunday

The Daily Journal

Notes & Records

Speedwell

Week ....

Opposite, Raining

NOVEMBER
CELIA THAXTER

THERE is no wind at all to-night
　　To dash the drops against the
　　　pane;
No sound abroad, nor any light;
　　And softly falls the autumn rain.

There is no color in the world,
　　No lovely tint on hill or plain;
The summer's golden sails are
　　furled;
　　And softly falls the autumn rain.

The earth lies tacitly beneath,
　　As it were dead to joy or pain;
It does not move, it does not
　　breathe;
　　And softly falls the autumn rain.

And all my heart is patient too.
　　I wait till it shall wake again;
For songs of Spring shall sound
　　anew
　　Though sadly falls the autumn
　　　rain.

Monday

The Daily Journal

Tuesday

The Daily Journal

Wednesday

The Daily Journal

Thursday

The Daily Journal

Friday

The Daily Journal

Saturday

The Daily Journal

Sunday

The Daily Journal

Week ....

Month   *Dates*

Monday

The Daily Journal

Tuesday

The Daily Journal

Wednesday

The Daily Journal

Thursday

The Daily Journal

Friday

The Daily Journal

Saturday

The Daily Journal

Sunday

The Daily Journal

Apple

Month	Dates	Week ....

Monday

The Daily Journal

Tuesday

The Daily Journal

Wednesday

The Daily Journal

Thursday

The Daily Journal

Friday

The Daily Journal

Saturday

The Daily Journal

Sunday

The Daily Journal

Notes & Records

Week ....

Month   *Dates*

Notes & Records

Monday	*The Daily Journal*
Tuesday	*The Daily Journal*
Wednesday	*The Daily Journal*
Thursday	*The Daily Journal*
Friday	*The Daily Journal*
Saturday	*The Daily Journal*
Sunday	*The Daily Journal*

Month	*Dates*

Monday

The Daily Journal

Tuesday

The Daily Journal

Wednesday

The Daily Journal

Thursday

The Daily Journal

Friday

The Daily Journal

Saturday

The Daily Journal

Sunday

The Daily Journal

The Sweet Violet

S hakespeare alludes to Violets in Twelfth Night he makes the Duke ask the musicians to repeat

> *"That strain again; it had a dying fall:*
> *Oh, it came o'er my ear like the sweet south,*
> *That breathes upon a bank of violets,*
> *Stealing, and giving odour."*

Chaucer, Herrick, Shelley, Scott, and Tennyson, all mention this flower; so also Tom Hood, who says,"The violet is a Nun." And do we not all know Wordsworth's exquisite lines—

> *"A violet by a mossy stone*
> *Half hidden from the eye !*
> *Fair as a star when only one*
> *Is shining in the sky."?*

Illustrated opposite is *V. Odorata*. One of a number of species commonly found.

Week ....

Notes & Records

Month   *Dates*

Monday
The Daily Journal

Tuesday
The Daily Journal

Wednesday
The Daily Journal

Thursday
The Daily Journal

Friday
The Daily Journal

Saturday
The Daily Journal

Sunday
The Daily Journal

Month	*Dates*	*Week* ....

Monday

The Daily Journal

Notes & Records

Tuesday

The Daily Journal

Wednesday

The Daily Journal

Thursday

The Daily Journal

Friday

The Daily Journal

Saturday

The Daily Journal

Sunday

The Daily Journal

Month	*Dates*	*Week* ....

Monday

The Daily Journal

Tuesday

The Daily Journal

Wednesday

The Daily Journal

Thursday

The Daily Journal

Friday

The Daily Journal

Saturday

The Daily Journal

Sunday

The Daily Journal

FLOWERS IN OCTOBER
CELIA THAXTER

THE cricket is hoarse in the faded grass,
The low bush rustles so thin and sere,
Swift overhead the small birds pass
With songs that are lonely and sweet
and clear.

The last chill asters their petals fold,
And gone is the morning-glory's bell,
But close in a loving hand I hold
Long sprays of the scarlet pimpernel.

And thick at my feet are blossom
and leaf,
Blossoms rich red as the robes
of kings,
Hardly they're touched by the
autumn's grief
—Do they surmise what the
winter brings ?

I turn my eyes from the sweet,
sad sky,
From the foam-white gulls and the
sails that gleam,
To muse on the scattered flowers
that lie
Lost as yet in a summer dream.

O darlings ! nursed by the salt
sea-spray !
O shapes of beauty so quaint
and bright !
But for a little the frosts delay;
Soon will be ended your brief delight.

Could I but succor you every one,
Spread wings of safety 'twixt harm
and you,—
Call from its southern travel the sun,
Banish the snow from
the arching blue !

It may not be: and the frosts must fall,
The winter must reign in the
summer's stead;
But though you perish beyond recall,
Ever I love you, alive or dead.

Week ....

Notes & Records

Month   *Dates*

Monday   *The Daily Journal*

Tuesday   *The Daily Journal*

Wednesday   *The Daily Journal*

Thursday   *The Daily Journal*

Friday   *The Daily Journal*

Saturday   *The Daily Journal*

Sunday   *The Daily Journal*

Month	*Dates*	*Week* ....

Monday

The Daily Journal

Tuesday

The Daily Journal

Wednesday

The Daily Journal

Thursday

The Daily Journal

Friday

The Daily Journal

Saturday

The Daily Journal

Sunday

The Daily Journal

Opposite, Hoar Frost

"DOWN TO SLEEP"
H.H.

NOVEMBER *woods are bare and still,*
November days are clear and bright;
Each noon burns up the morning's
chill;
The morning's snow is gone by night;
Each day my steps grow slow, grow
light,
As through the woods I reverent creep,
Watching all things lie "down to
sleep."

I never knew before what beds,
Fragrant to smell, and soft to touch,
The forest sifts and shapes and
spreads;
I never knew before how much
Of human sound there is in such
Low tones as through the forest sweep
When all wild things lie "down to
sleep."

Each day I find new coverlids
Tucked in, and more sweet eyes shut
tight;
Sometimes the viewless mother bids
Her ferns kneel down, full in my
sight;
I hear their chorus of "good night".
And half I smile, and half I weep,
Listening while they lie "down to
sleep."

November woods are bare and still;
November days are bright and good;
Life's noon burns up life's morning
chill;
Life's night rests feet which long have
stood;
Some warm, soft bed, in field or wood,
The mother will not fail to keep,
Where we can "lay us down to sleep."

Month   *Dates*

The Harebell

S ir Walter Scott treats our dainty flower tenderly and lovingly, and evidently he admired its sprightly grace and elasticity, for he writes:

"E'en the slight Harebell raised its head

Elastic from her airy tread."

and we all know that no soft and pulpy "Bluebell" or Hyacinth could have done that. Again he writes:

"For me, she stooped, and, looking round,

Plucked a blue Harebell from the ground.

This little flower that loves the lea

May well my simple emblem be;

It drinks Heaven's dews, blithe as a Rose

That in the King's own garden grows."

Lastly, we find Tennyson alluding to some mountain variety as follows:—

"Love like an Alpine Harebell hung with tears,

By some cold warning glacier."

About a hundred species of this genus are known, and many of them are cultivated in our gardens. Some of the Alpine species are very lovely and bear blue, purple, or white flowers.

Monday

The Daily Journal

Tuesday

The Daily Journal

Wednesday

The Daily Journal

Thursday

The Daily Journal

Friday

The Daily Journal

Saturday

The Daily Journal

Sunday

The Daily Journal

Week ....

Notes & Records

Month   *Dates*

Monday

The Daily Journal

Tuesday

The Daily Journal

Wednesday

The Daily Journal

Thursday

The Daily Journal

Friday

The Daily Journal

Saturday

The Daily Journal

Sunday

The Daily Journal

Month	Dates	Week ....

Monday

The Daily Journal

Tuesday

The Daily Journal

Wednesday

The Daily Journal

Thursday

The Daily Journal

Friday

The Daily Journal

Saturday

The Daily Journal

Sunday

The Daily Journal

Notes & Records

The Foxglove

Wordsworth, strikes a firm and true note—

"Bees that soar for bloom,
High as the highest peak of
Furness Fells,
Will murmur by the hour in
Foxglove bells."

Tennyson calls them "dappled bells," and Eliza Cook invites the soft winds to ring—

"A fairy chime Upon
Foxglove bells."

And it is an old and quaint conceit that the towering spire of a Foxglove is "a belfry for the fairies." Again, we are told that this flower is emblematic of insincerity, because although externally so beautiful its juices are poisonous; still this very poisonous or active principle now known as digitaline, is one of the most potent remedies in the hands of skilled physicans, and has done much to assuage and relieve those suffering from affections of the heart. There are, at least, a dozen species or more of the genus, but our own is by far the handsomest of them all, especially the dark-spotted purple, and the cream-coloured and snow-white forms. We have seen a white variety totally devoid of spots, and now and then a monstrous form appears having the topmost flowers on the raceme, regular and erect, something like a Campanula.

Monday

The Daily Journal

Tuesday

The Daily Journal

Wednesday

The Daily Journal

Thursday

The Daily Journal

Friday

The Daily Journal

Saturday

The Daily Journal

Sunday

The Daily Journal

By L. Clarkson.

They are standing sheeted
In the dark
Of the year completed,
White and stark.
Through the forest roams the
lonely crow;
Gone are all the homes he
Used to know.
For the nests were blown down
In the Fall,
When the grass was mown down
Ripe and tall.

Through the   pines and larches
On the   hill
Many a storm   cloud marches
Grim and   chill.
And the North   wind bends the
Oak's bald   crown,
Many chaplets   sends he
Shivering   down.
But the fir   is happy
In the storm.
His dark covering wraps he
Close and warm.
Of all trees, the fairest
Maple stands,
Saddest, coldest, barest,
With her hands
Stretched out, asking cover
Of the sun;
Till that faithless lover
Cold had grown.
But the phantom fingers
Of the beech,
Clutch the robe that lingers
Holding each
Wind-blown leaf that flutters
To be free.
In low voice he mutters
Ceaselessly:—
"All the singing Summer
I was green;
When the days grew dumber,
And the sheen
"Of their glory faded.
I was mute:
Long and late I shaded
My slim root.
"But my foliage lighter
Daily grew,
And the sunshine, whiter
Filtering through.
"Now my noonday garment,
Threadbare, white,
Still shall be my cerement
Through the night
"In my pride I know no
Vigor done.
To the world I show no
Skeleton.
"When my resurrection
Robes are green,
In my new perfection
High, serene,
"I shall stand and wear my
Honors best.
But I will not bare my
Naked breast
"To the curious wer...
There are gnome wer...
"We say your...

"For the Spring delaying
Makes us late,
While the flow'rs go Maying,
We must wait.
But we will not waver
At each gust;
Ah! the trees were braver
Flowers would tr...
So the phantom tr...
Bear th...
Man...

Month	Dates	Week ....

Monday

The Daily Journal

Tuesday

The Daily Journal

Wednesday

The Daily Journal

Thursday

The Daily Journal

Friday

The Daily Journal

Saturday

The Daily Journal

Sunday

The Daily Journal

AUTUMN HYMN
RICHARD H. NEWELL

CHANGING, *fading, falling, flying*
From the homes that gave them birth,
Autumn leaves, in beauty dying,
Seek the mother-breast of Earth.

Soon shall all the songless wood
Shiver in the deepening snow,
Mourning in its solitude
Like some Rachel in her woe.

Slowly sinks yon evening sun,
Softly wanes the cheerful light,
And, the twelve hours' labor done,
Onward comes the solemn night.

So, on many a home of gladness
Falls, O Death, thy winter gloom;
Stands there still in doubt and sadness
Many a Mary at the tomb.

But the genial Spring returning
Will the sylvan pomp renew;
And the new-born flame of morning
Kindle rainbows in the dew.

So shall God, His promise keeping,
To the world by Jesus given,
Wake our loved ones, sweetly sleeping,
At the opening dawn of heaven.

Light from darkness! Life from death !
Dies the body, not the soul.
From the chrysalis beneath
Soars the spirit to its goal.

Opposite, an old stone vase

Those mossy flagged walks where bygone generations have trod; those richly-coloured old brick walls, to which the old-fashioned clematis and roses cling lovingly as of yore. Everywhere an old-world charm that the flight of Time has enhanced rather than lessened, for with the passing years the girth and beauty of those majestic trees have increased, and everything has settled into a great harmonious "whole" impossible to find in the most carefully planned new garden. Some of my earliest recollections are of an old garden I used to visit in very tender years; and its beauty so impressed my childish mind that I can see it plainly before me even now. A broad flight of stone steps, mossy green and splashed with orange-coloured lichens, led down from the casement windows of the old red-brick house, over a smooth, sloping lawn gay with flower beds, to where beyond, in the orchard, one came upon the remnant of an old-time moat, its still surface thickly studded with water-lilies white and yellow, over which the ancient apple-trees bent their gnarled and whitened trunks, in spring shedding a shower of rosy petals into the water below.

Monday

The Daily Journal

Tuesday

The Daily Journal

Wednesday

The Daily Journal

Thursday

The Daily Journal

Friday

The Daily Journal

Saturday

The Daily Journal

Sunday

The Daily Journal

An old
Stone Vase

APRIL'S GARLAND

Month	Dates	Week ....

Monday

The Daily Journal

Tuesday

The Daily Journal

Wednesday

The Daily Journal

Thursday

The Daily Journal

Friday

The Daily Journal

Saturday

The Daily Journal

Sunday

The Daily Journal

Month   *Dates*

The White Water Lily

The Japanese, so fond of flowers, generally set a peculiarly high value on the Water lily, which is one of their emblems of purity because its flowers are always unsullied even though the plant may grow in muddy water. This exquisite flower is found all over Europe, and the Greeks dedicated it to their water-nymphs, and like the Egyptians used its flowers amongst their offerings to the dead. All through the East, Water-lilies blue and red and white, are highly prized, especially in Cashmere. These flowers have a habit of closing their petals and sinking into the water at night, or after sundown, from which they emerge fresh and fair soon after sunrise. Fresh and fair in the opening bud stage, but few of our native flowers can equal those of this Nymphaea in texture and beauty of form, there being a purity of petal, and a sculpturesque kind of beauty about them not easy to describe. Now and then variations in size occur amongst a batch of natural seedlings, and in a lake in Sweden a very rare rose-coloured form is found. A sweet-scented Nymphaea is not uncommon in North America, and a pink or rosy-petalled form of that species is found at Cape Cod, whence it has been sent to our gardens.

Monday

The Daily Journal

Tuesday

The Daily Journal

Wednesday

The Daily Journal

Thursday

The Daily Journal

Friday

The Daily Journal

Saturday

The Daily Journal

Sunday

The Daily Journal

Week ....

Month

Dates

Notes & Records

Monday

The Daily Journal

Tuesday

The Daily Journal

Wednesday

The Daily Journal

Thursday

The Daily Journal

Friday

The Daily Journal

Saturday

The Daily Journal

Sunday

The Daily Journal

Month   *Dates*   *Week* ....

Monday	*The Daily Journal*
Tuesday	*The Daily Journal*
Wednesday	*The Daily Journal*
Thursday	*The Daily Journal*
Friday	*The Daily Journal*
Saturday	*The Daily Journal*
Sunday	*The Daily Journal*

Week ....

Notes & Records

Month   *Dates*

Monday

The Daily Journal

Tuesday

The Daily Journal

Wednesday

The Daily Journal

Thursday

The Daily Journal

Friday

The Daily Journal

Saturday

The Daily Journal

Sunday

The Daily Journal

Wild Strawberry

Monday

The Daily Journal

Tuesday

The Daily Journal

Wednesday

The Daily Journal

Thursday

The Daily Journal

Friday

The Daily Journal

Saturday

The Daily Journal

Sunday

The Daily Journal

SEPTEMBER
GILBERT NASH

CHANGED is the verdure of the
    branching trees;
The fading leaves desert the
    sturdy oak,
The brilliant maple through the
    autumn smoke,
And yellow walnut waving in
    the breeze,
The fadeless pines that thickly stud
    the leas
With the deep crimson of the
    sumach vie,
While all the varied tints of earth
    and sky
Share the rich beauty of the
    changeless seas.
Gone is the comeliness of flowery June
    And the fierce heat of July's
    fervid sun;
The languid August air is felt
    no more;
The ripening influence of
    September's noon
And cooler nights, proclaim the
    summer done;
That the fair harvest time will soon
    be o'er.

The Meadow Buttercup

There are few sights more inspiriting to those born and reared in the town than the occasional sight of the fresh, lush meadows in May when the grass is golden with the flowers of the "Crow Flower," or "Buttercup," as shown in our plate. There is no sure and certain proof, but it may be taken on trust, that Shakespeare referred to this plant in *Love's Labour's Lost,* Act v. Scene 2, when he sings,

> "And Cuckoo buds of yellow hue
> Do paint the meadows
>   with delight."

Phillips in his ever interesting *Flora Historica* is so much taken up with the garden Ranunculus in all its variety that he can scarcely spare a word for our native kinds; still he does inform us that the "Upright Meadow Crowfoot" with double flowers goes by the popular name of "Yellow Bachelor's Buttons," a fit companion in the garden for the double white continental Buttercup known as "Fair Maids of France." There is very little poetry about the Buttercup, but Clare in his *Rural Life and Scenery,* alludes to the "good little people," and to this flower when he sings

> And fairies now, no doubt unseen
>   In silent revels sup.
> Witn dew-drop bumpers toast
>   their Queen,
> From Crow-flower's golden cup.

Monday

The Daily Journal

Tuesday

The Daily Journal

Wednesday

The Daily Journal

Thursday

The Daily Journal

Friday

The Daily Journal

Saturday

The Daily Journal

Sunday

The Daily Journal

In an old Garden

Holly-hocks

Month	Dates	Week ....

Monday

The Daily Journal

Tuesday

The Daily Journal

Wednesday

The Daily Journal

Thursday

The Daily Journal

Friday

The Daily Journal

Saturday

The Daily Journal

Sunday

The Daily Journal

	Month	Dates	Week ....
Monday	*The Daily Journal*		
Tuesday	*The Daily Journal*		
Wednesday	*The Daily Journal*		
Thursday	*The Daily Journal*		
Friday	*The Daily Journal*		
Saturday	*The Daily Journal*		
Sunday	*The Daily Journal*		

The Convolvulus

The name Convolvulus, often applied to the plant we illustrate, is in allusion to its twining or binding habit of growth, one of its rustic names also being "Bearbind." Another country appellation is "Hedge Lily," in which connection we may remember Pliny's quaint saying, "That Nature in learning to form a Lily turned out a Convolvulus." Miss Anne Pratt, who years ago wrote a most interesting work on wild flowers, tells us that this Bindweed twines itself in a way contrary to the sun—i.e., from right to left; and not from left to right, as is the case with the "Black Bryony". Why two of our common hedgerow plants should thus differ in their habit or direction of climbing is a question you may ask yourselves as you look at them and get their answer if you can ! This is how botanical knowledge is gained; you simply ask the plants a question, and carefully watch them until you win the secret from them. You may peep into Mr. Darwin's book on *Climbing Plants*, in which he especially alludes to this question of twining, and how it is of use to the plants which have adopted this method of getting their full share of air and light, which is in some ways even more essential than root-space and earth food.

Week ....

Opposite, falling leaves

  AUTUMN.

WE, too, have our Autumns when
 our leaves
Drop loosely through the
 dampened air;
When all our good seems bound
 in sheaves
And we stand reaped and bare.

Our seasons have no fixed
 returns;
Without our will they come
 and go;
At noon our sudden
 Summer burns—
Ere sunset, all is snow.

But each day brings less
 Summer cheer,
Cramps more our ineffectual
 Springs,
And something earlier, every year,
 Our singing birds take wings.

Monday

The Daily Journal

Tuesday

The Daily Journal

Wednesday

The Daily Journal

Thursday

The Daily Journal

Friday

The Daily Journal

Saturday

The Daily Journal

Sunday

The Daily Journal

L. Clarkson

An old garden – a brick bridge, flanked with somewhat dilapidated statuary and vases, spanned the moat, and everywhere the mosses, lichens, and clustering ivy gave an added grace and charm. It is long since I saw that old garden the friends who owned it have passed away but I have often wondered if subsequent owners have appreciated its dignified early eighteenth century air, or whether it has been fatally tidied up and "improved" to suit more modern ideas! In such a garden are studies in plenty the old-fashioned white cluster rose and "maiden's-blush" climbing over a rustic arch; the "herbaceous border" sunning under the warm brick wall, the sturdy buttresses of which are almost hidden with masses of purple and white clematis in luxurious profusion; the water-lilies with their broad flat leaves in large patches on the surface of the moat, breaking the reflections of blue sky and dark trees. In a little corner in a garden like this you have a study before you full of joy and delight. That tall spike of madonna lilies, standing so freshly white against the deep rich tones of the closely-cropped yew hedge, makes a picture in itself; or that group of hollyhocks, showing out clearly against the sky as we see it from our lowly seat on the grass.

Monday

The Daily Journal

Tuesday

The Daily Journal

Wednesday

The Daily Journal

Thursday

The Daily Journal

Friday

The Daily Journal

Saturday

The Daily Journal

Sunday

The Daily Journal

The same flower
(½ hour later.)

LIBERTY
(A red, red rose)

Monday

The Daily Journal

Tuesday

The Daily Journal

Wednesday

The Daily Journal

Thursday

The Daily Journal

Friday

The Daily Journal

Saturday

The Daily Journal

Sunday

The Daily Journal

The Rose

I think, for a beginning, it would be well to make a study of the humble little wild rose of the hedgerow. There is plenty of scope for careful drawing in this flower without our having to contend with the difficulties of the multiplicity of petals possessed by her prouder sisters of the garden. Note the flimsy nature of the flower, and how delicate pink shades to creamy white. It is an education in rose drawing to go round and note the wonderful difference of form in well-known varieties. There is a Gloire de Dijon (or "Glory," as the gardener dubs it), cup-like and solid in form, with its petals curving back in fascinating little points; here is the old-world "Maiden's blush," very flat when fully developed; the "Niphetos," with its tulip-shaped petals and drooping habit, bending over so modestly that one has almost to kneel before it to see its lotus-like beauty; "Catherine Mermet," "La France," "Malmaison," and a host of others, each with some special character of form. Suppose we take one of the tea-rose family for our study. I choose this especially because of its wonderful variety of colour, distinction of form, and also perhaps as a little bit of personal sentiment, as a group of these self-same flowers was the very first picture I ever exhibited and sold.

Month   *Dates*

Roses

Aspray of rose-leaves is a very beautiful study. Take a single leaf first and study its shape noting not only its form of five leaflets, but the way they are arranged on the stem. The serrations on the leaves require care, they are not a mere jagged edge, but each little spine points towards the tip of the leaf. Then again notice the position of the thorns on the stem; they are somewhat hooked in shape, the prickly part pointing downwards. Nature has a special purpose in arranging them thus, as they defy the approach of predatory insects.

Monday

The Daily Journal

Tuesday

The Daily Journal

Wednesday

The Daily Journal

Thursday

The Daily Journal

Friday

The Daily Journal

Saturday

The Daily Journal

Sunday

The Daily Journal

Week ....

Notes & Records	Month	Dates

Monday

The Daily Journal

Tuesday

The Daily Journal

Wednesday

The Daily Journal

Thursday

The Daily Journal

Friday

The Daily Journal

Saturday

The Daily Journal

Sunday

The Daily Journal

Month	Dates	Week ....

Monday

The Daily Journal

Notes & Records

Tuesday

The Daily Journal

Wednesday

The Daily Journal

Thursday

The Daily Journal

Friday

The Daily Journal

Saturday

The Daily Journal

Sunday

The Daily Journal

The Lychnis or Campion

The common red Lychnis or Campion is frequently to be met with growing on the margins of damp meadows, in hedges, or copses, or in the more open and sunny parts of woods. The white kind prefers shady positions, and is also very common. Both belong to the same natural order as the Pinks and Carnations, and Sweet Williams of our gardens, the Saponarias or "Soap.worts," the Stitch-worts, "Corn Cockle" and "Catchflies," and "Chick weeds," of our fields. A very near relative is *Lychnis Flos Cuculi* or "The Ragged Robin," of our woods and hedges, which has its rosy petals much divided, or cut up into narrow shreds. This flower comes with the cuckoo in early summer, hence its Latin name Flos cuculi.

Monday

The Daily Journal

Tuesday

The Daily Journal

Wednesday

The Daily Journal

Thursday

The Daily Journal

Friday

The Daily Journal

Saturday

The Daily Journal

Sunday

The Daily Journal

Month	*Dates*

Monday

The Daily Journal

Tuesday

The Daily Journal

Wednesday

The Daily Journal

Thursday

The Daily Journal

Friday

The Daily Journal

Saturday

The Daily Journal

Sunday

The Daily Journal

Honeysuckle

Both popular names— viz., Woodbine or "Woodbind," and "Honeysuckle"—have been applied to other twining plants, as well as to those having honeyed flowers or nectaries, or a twining habit of growth. But to-day both names are in the main devoted to the plant Mr. Moon has so well represented in the plate before us. In both English and Irish woods we have seen fine old examples of this Lonicera fully fifty feet high, scrambling up the trunks and branches of Scotch Fir, Larch, and Birch trees, its twisted rope-like stems all entangled below, and bringing to mind the great roots and llianas that are such a distinct feature in tropical forests. Beautiful in form,and exquisite in fragrance as it assuredly is, it is a plant for the rustic cottage porch or pergola, or the woodman's hut, rather than for the classic portico, for to see it at its best, it must not be restricted to the level of neatness or prim lines, but demands, even under cultivation, that freedom and grace of movement which, in nature, it ever enjoys.

Week ....

Notes & Records

Month   Dates

Sycamore

Monday	The Daily Journal	
Tuesday	The Daily Journal	
Wednesday	The Daily Journal	
Thursday	The Daily Journal	
Friday	The Daily Journal	
Saturday	The Daily Journal	
Sunday	The Daily Journal	

A Rosetree in full bearing

Month	**Dates**

Monday

The Daily Journal

Tuesday

The Daily Journal

Wednesday

The Daily Journal

Thursday

The Daily Journal

Friday

The Daily Journal

Saturday

The Daily Journal

Sunday

The Daily Journal

Childhood

Ever since my childhood, wild flowers have held a great charm for me, and I can remember how, in those golden hours of long ago, I used to steal away through a hole in the hedge of my country home, known only to the chickens and myself, to the forbidden ground of a neighbouring meadow, and there revel in the long, and often damp, grass, with its treasures of golden buttercups and dandelions, and its high cow-parsley towering above my limited stature. Here I would remain until found and reprimanded by those in authority over me, and condemned to the tamer delights of the garden, with its trim lawns and gravelled walks.

Painting

My first essay into water-colour painting was, I grieve to say, a surreptitious one. I had been punished for some childish indiscretion, by being shut in an empty room, my captors forgetting that a door communicating with my father's study was open. Here, indeed, was food for wonder and delight. Models of ships, curios of various kinds, hitherto out of reach, I fingered with the enthusiasm of a true daughter of Eve for forbidden fruit. But the greatest joy of all was to discover that my naughty podgy little fingers could slide back the lid of the old-fashioned mahogany colour-box, and so disclose to view the treasures within. Could a youthful soul with artistic longing withstand so great a temptation ? I commenced a series of hasty "impressions" on note-paper, letters, anything I could find about, hurriedly throwing them behind the writing table to avoid detection. And although a speedy retribution followed, for of course these works of Art were discovered when the room was swept, I still remember that hour of stolen joy as one of the happiest in my life.

Monday

The Daily Journal

Tuesday

The Daily Journal

Wednesday

The Daily Journal

Thursday

The Daily Journal

Friday

The Daily Journal

Saturday

The Daily Journal

Sunday

The Daily Journal

Month	Dates	Week ....

Monday

The Daily Journal

Tuesday

The Daily Journal

Wednesday

The Daily Journal

Thursday

The Daily Journal

Friday

The Daily Journal

Saturday

The Daily Journal

Sunday

The Daily Journal

Ivy

Month	Dates	Week ....

Monday

The Daily Journal

Tuesday

The Daily Journal

Wednesday

The Daily Journal

Thursday

The Daily Journal

Friday

The Daily Journal

Saturday

The Daily Journal

Sunday

The Daily Journal

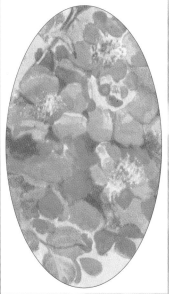

Roses

Our business to day is to paint roses, not merely to talk of them, so, if you have your nicely-washed palette and materials in readiness, let us start without further generalities: only you must not feel discouraged if I warn you that the task on which you have embarked is not an easy one ! Not only is the rose one of the most beautiful and fascinating of flower studies, but one of the most difficult as well. We start, perhaps, a careful drawing of a half-opened bud, and even as we work its form is changing before our eyes, and the rose is opening her heart to the rays of light and warmth as they fall on her from the window. We must lose no time in sketching her in boldly before she alters too much, even if we have to finish the details from memory or another flower. When called away whilst painting roses (if only for a few minutes) I always carefully cover them up from the light. A cardboard box (if sufficiently large) will prove a very efficient screen.

Monday

The Daily Journal

Tuesday

The Daily Journal

Wednesday

The Daily Journal

Thursday

The Daily Journal

Friday

The Daily Journal

Saturday

The Daily Journal

Sunday

The Daily Journal

Ring·a·Ring O'Roses

	Month	Dates	Week ....
Monday	*The Daily Journal*		*Notes & Records*
Tuesday	*The Daily Journal*		
Wednesday	*The Daily Journal*		
Thursday	*The Daily Journal*		
Friday	*The Daily Journal*		**Daffodils**
Saturday	*The Daily Journal*		
Sunday	*The Daily Journal*		

Week ....

Notes & Records

A posy with Primroses

Monday	*The Daily Journal*
Tuesday	*The Daily Journal*
Wednesday	*The Daily Journal*
Thursday	*The Daily Journal*
Friday	*The Daily Journal*
Saturday	*The Daily Journal*
Sunday	*The Daily Journal*

	Month	Dates	Week ....
Monday	The Daily Journal		Notes & Records
Tuesday	The Daily Journal		
Wednesday	The Daily Journal		
Thursday	The Daily Journal		
Friday	The Daily Journal		
Saturday	The Daily Journal		
Sunday	The Daily Journal		

Week ....

Notes & Records

Monday

The Daily Journal

Tuesday

The Daily Journal

Wednesday

The Daily Journal

Thursday

The Daily Journal

Friday

The Daily Journal

Meadow Buttercup

Saturday

The Daily Journal

Sunday

The Daily Journal

Month	Dates	Week ....

Monday

The Daily Journal

Tuesday

The Daily Journal

Wednesday

The Daily Journal

Woodruff

Thursday

The Daily Journal

Friday

The Daily Journal

Saturday

The Daily Journal

Sunday

The Daily Journal

Month	*Dates*	*Week* ....

Monday	*The Daily Journal*
Tuesday	*The Daily Journal*
Wednesday	*The Daily Journal*
Thursday	*The Daily Journal*
Friday	*The Daily Journal*
Saturday	*The Daily Journal*
Sunday	*The Daily Journal*

County walks

Following the advice of the famous cookery book, to "first catch your hare," let us start in quest of our little models. Let us don our thickest boots and, armed with a sketchbook, and an ancient pair of leather gloves, in which we may grub delightfully in damp earth regardless of consequences, brave the muddy lane, with its wild, untrimmed hedgerows, high banks, and deep ditches. There, in a tangle of frost-tinted ivy, red-brown beech leaves, feathery moss, prickly brambles, and lichen-coated twigs, we shall surely see the objects of our search. And let us notice, for future reference, the wonderful effect the changing sky has on them, perhaps more especially on the leaves. That great inky rain-cloud throws a cold grey shadow, and everything reflects a sombre hue; but now the raindrops have fallen and the bright spring sunshine beams forth again, the violet leaves, glistening with liquid diamonds, are dancing with delight in the breeze, a golden green that would defy the brightest mixture of emerald and aureolin our palettes could offer.

Week ....

Month *Dates*

Notes & Records

Rose bowl

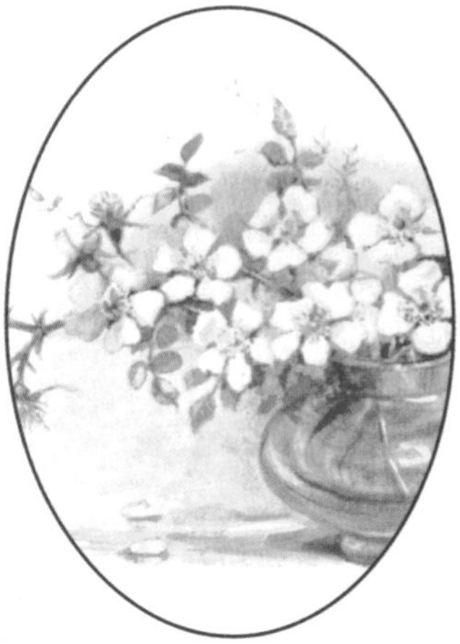

Monday	*The Daily Journal*
Tuesday	*The Daily Journal*
Wednesday	*The Daily Journal*
Thursday	*The Daily Journal*
Friday	*The Daily Journal*
Saturday	*The Daily Journal*
Sunday	*The Daily Journal*

Dead
Nettle

The Old
Gate-post